Build Sirius Black and help him escape from the Dementors!

After spending the summer holidays at his aunt and uncle's house, Harry was pleased to see Ron and Hermione again. Divide the grid into four groups of all three of the friends.

Look at the magical wanted posters made after
Sirius Black's escape from Azkaban.
Find two that are identical.

What is lurking behind the frosted window?
Colour in the picture using the key to solve this
dark mystery.

It's going to be a tough ride on the Hogwarts Express!
Match the square to where it should be on the track.
That's where the Dementors will stop the train!

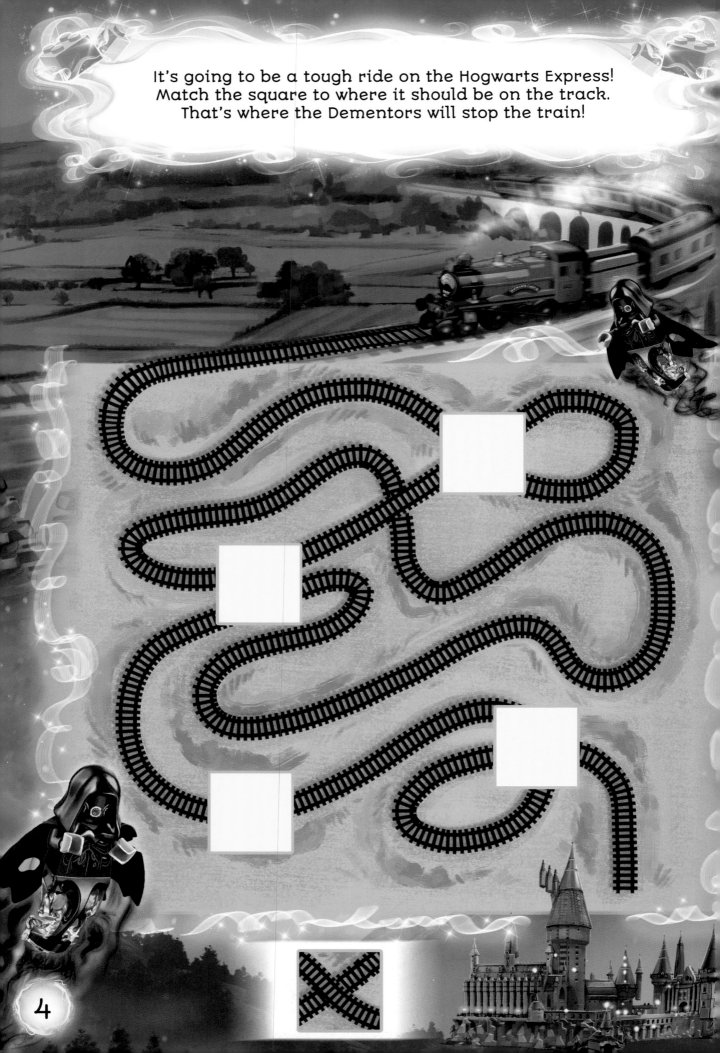

Oops, Harry has eaten an exploding bonbon! Find other treats that should be avoided by outlining three identical sweets found next to each other in the grid.

Ron's pet, Scabbers, is veeeery old for a rat. Count up all the rodents to find out how long he has been the Weasley family's pet.

=

Is it possible to go to two classes taking place at the same time? It is for Hermione! Look for the route shown in the box to find out which classes she is running to.

KEY

1 2 3

4 5

A
Divination + Ancient Runes

Hang on. That's not possible.

B
Care of Magical Creatures + Potions

C
Defence Against the Dark Arts + Transfiguration

Time for a Divination test! Find the teacup that is different from the others – at its bottom Harry found a grim prophecy.

Match the shadow to the right portrait and you'll find out who Harry saw in the crystal ball.

A   B   C   D

Hagrid has arranged for the students to meet a Hippogriff! Try his Care of Magical Creatures class and spot eight differences between the two pictures.

According to the *Daily Prophet*, Sirius Black has been seen near Hogwarts! Work out which students were gripped by the sensational article. Match them to the right pictures.

A B C D E

You don't think he'd come to Hogwarts, do you?

What will the *Riddikulus* spell turn this enormous spider into? Match up the colour wheel next to the spider to find out.

What really finishes a Boggart is laughter.

The Fat Lady's portrait without ... the Fat Lady?
Surely not! Use the clues to find out where the heroine
of the painting hid.

She's gone!

· This picture has a rectangular frame.
· It's a landscape with animals.
· Hogwarts doesn't appear in it.
· It shows animals without wings.

Draco has drawn a nasty picture of Harry.
Find out what it looks like by matching the small
picture pieces to the empty spaces.

The bad weather hasn't put off Quidditch fans. Find
out which team has more students by counting who
has more umbrellas. Gryffindor or Hufflepuff?

Will Harry Potter manage to catch the Golden Snitch?
Grab a pen and help him make it through the thick
clouds before the final whistle sounds.

START

FINISH

The Quidditch match didn't end well. Connect the close-ups to the right characters. The person without one didn't visit Harry in the hospital wing!

1 2 3 4 5

Oh, no! The Whomping Willow has destroyed Harry's broom! Help Ron put it back together by writing the letters of the parts in the empty spaces.

A C D B E F

Harry, there's something else you should know too. Well ...

It's a very cold and frosty winter at Hogwarts. Connect the dots to see who is soaring across the snowy sky.

Who gave Harry the Marauder's Map? Look at the patterns of portraits. Who is missing from each one? Draw numbers next to the right portraits at the bottom.

1

2

14   George   Ginny   Fred   Ron

Time for a secret trip to Hogsmeade! Help Harry put on the Invisibility Cloak – colour in the wizard so that he blends in with the background as much as possible.

The signpost of the most haunted house in England is covered in snow! Work out its name by finding the same shaped sign.

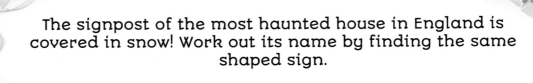

HOWLING SHACK

SHRIEKING SHACK

GROWLING SHACK

Making good snowballs isn't easy. But Harry made a perfect one, while he was under his Invisibility Cloak! Your turn! Finish the spiral to draw a snowball.

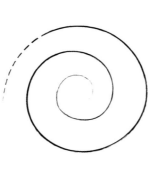

Harry went out for a night-time walk. Follow the instructions to lead the teachers through the hallways and work out which side they'll surprise Harry from.

Out for a little walk in the moonlight, are we?

The Marauder's Map is showing that someone long-lost is roaming around Hogwarts. None of the wands are pointing at the name of this person.

Albus Dumbledore

Sirius Black

Severus Snape

Remus Lupin

Minerva McGonagall

Peter Pettigrew

Malfoy looks worried! Look at the sequences below and choose which expression belongs in the blank space.

A   B   C

The student who isn't standing behind anyone faced Draco and made him flee in panic. Do you know who it was?

Professor McGonagall is an Animagus, which means she can change into an animal. The wizard who looks different on each portrait in the grid is one, too. Who is it?

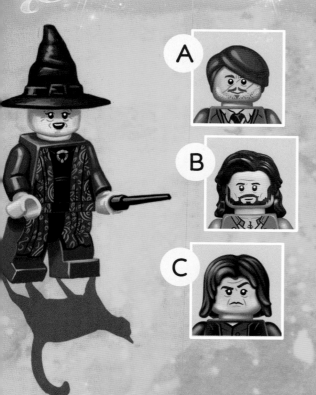

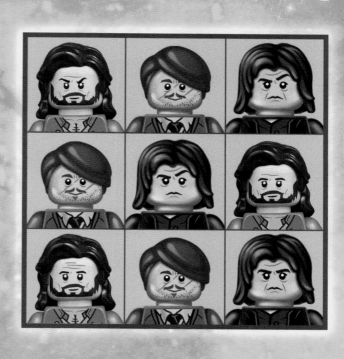

Lurking nearby is another Animagus. To find it, look at the close-up in the circle and match it to one of the pictures.

During a full moon, one of the teachers turns into something different. Find the portrait that isn't one of a pair. It shows who becomes a werewolf!

Buckbeak looks a bit faint. You can change that!
Use the example to help you finish the picture.

How many more Dementors will appear in the
night sky? Use the clues below to mark where
more of these terrifying creatures will pop up.

The orange squares show the
number of Dementors that are
touching them.
No two Dementors will appear in
squares that are touching each
other.

Harry and Hermione need to go back in time,
but for their mission to be successful they have
to make sure nobody sees them. Choose the pieces that
will help them.

Patronuses that take an animal form are the most powerful! Colour in shapes below each oval to make five different Patronuses in each set.

A

B

C

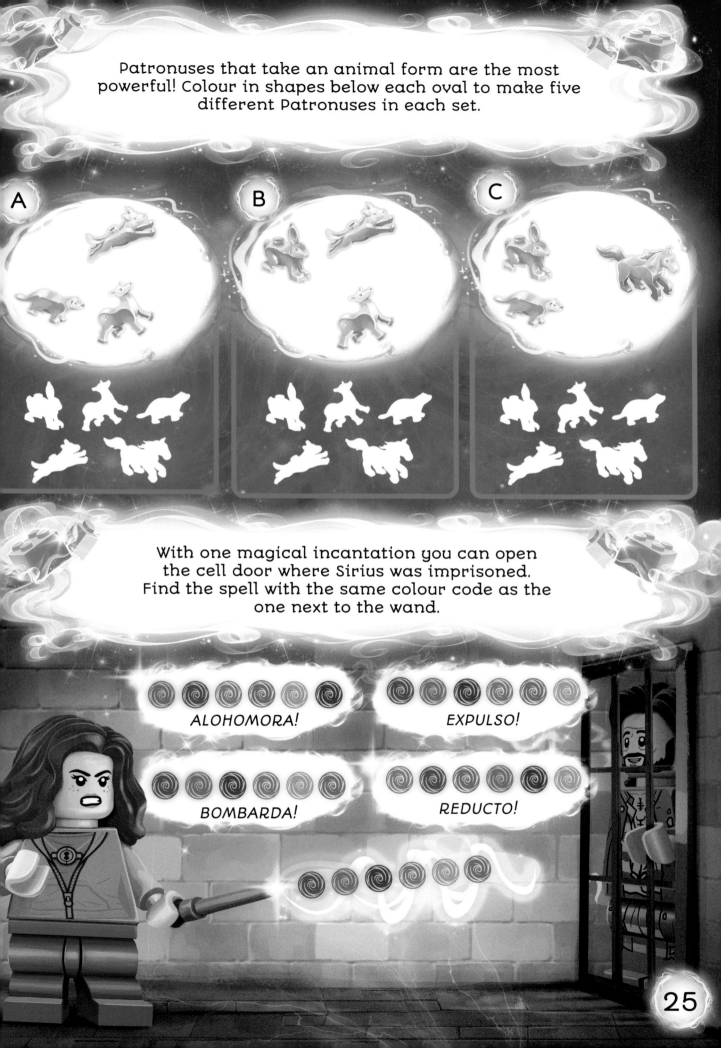

With one magical incantation you can open the cell door where Sirius was imprisoned. Find the spell with the same colour code as the one next to the wand.

ALOHOMORA!

EXPULSO!

BOMBARDA!

REDUCTO!

Despite being innocent, Sirius must remain in hiding.
Add the right number and letter coordinates under
each of the squares showing his potential hiding spots.

	A	B	C	D	E
1					
2					
3					
4					
5					

3E

Oops, Ron has opened Harry's present! Try to turn back time and mark the picture that shows the Firebolt as it would have looked all wrapped up.

But who sent it?

A

B

C

D

Lots of incredible birds live in the Owlery. Look at them closely and draw lines to connect the pairs of identical creatures.

Neville has found the entrance to the Room of Requirement. Follow both sets of arrows to help him open the two handles of the extraordinary door.

FINISH

START

START

28

Hermione was able to cast a Patronus Charm that looks like an otter. Lead the power of the spell from her wand to the Patronus. Use the squares at the bottom.

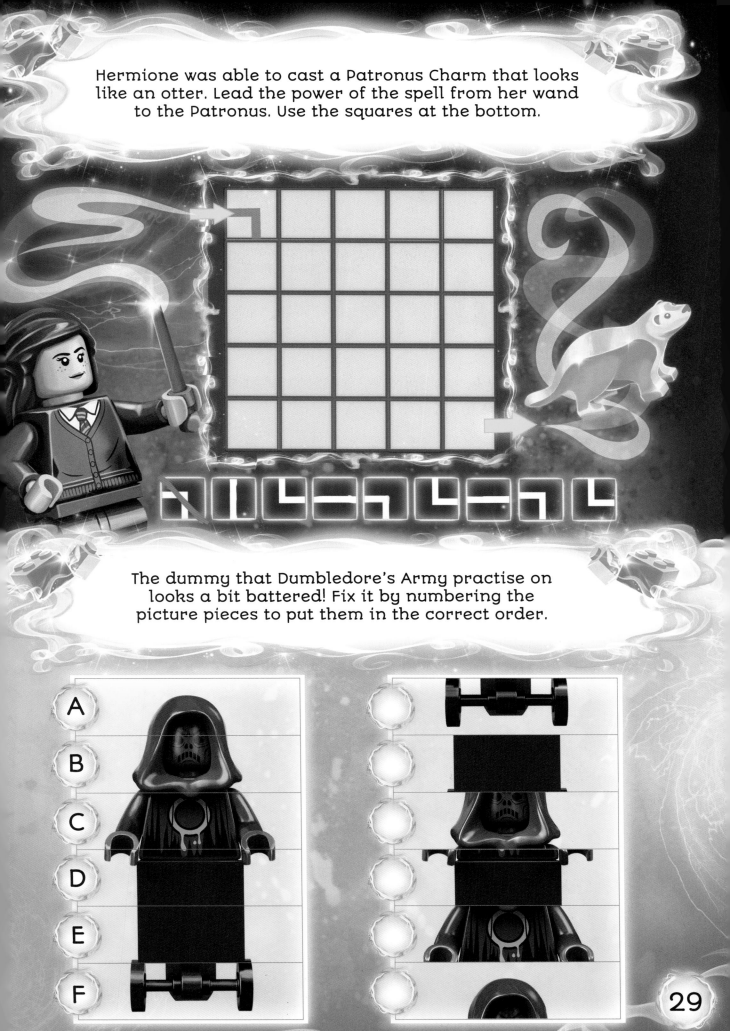

The dummy that Dumbledore's Army practise on looks a bit battered! Fix it by numbering the picture pieces to put them in the correct order.

A
B
C
D
E
F

Sirius Black's wanted poster isn't needed any more, so grab your pens and pencils and change it any way you like!

Answers

p. 2

p. 3

p. 4

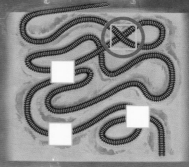

p. 5

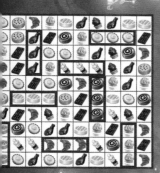

= 12

p. 6

A

p. 7

C

p. 9

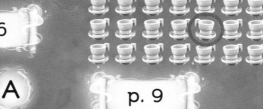

p. 9

p. 8

p. 10

p. 11

p. 12

p. 13

p. 14
p. 14
p. 16
p. 17

1   2

SHRIEKING SHACK

p. 19
p. 20

p. 18

Peter Pettigrew

A

A

p. 21

B

p. 22
p. 23

p. 24

X
1   3   1
X
X   3   X

1   2
3   4

p. 25
p. 26
p. 27

A
B
C

3E   3D   3A
1A   3B   5D

D

BOMBARDA!

p. 28
p. 29

F
E
B
D
C
A

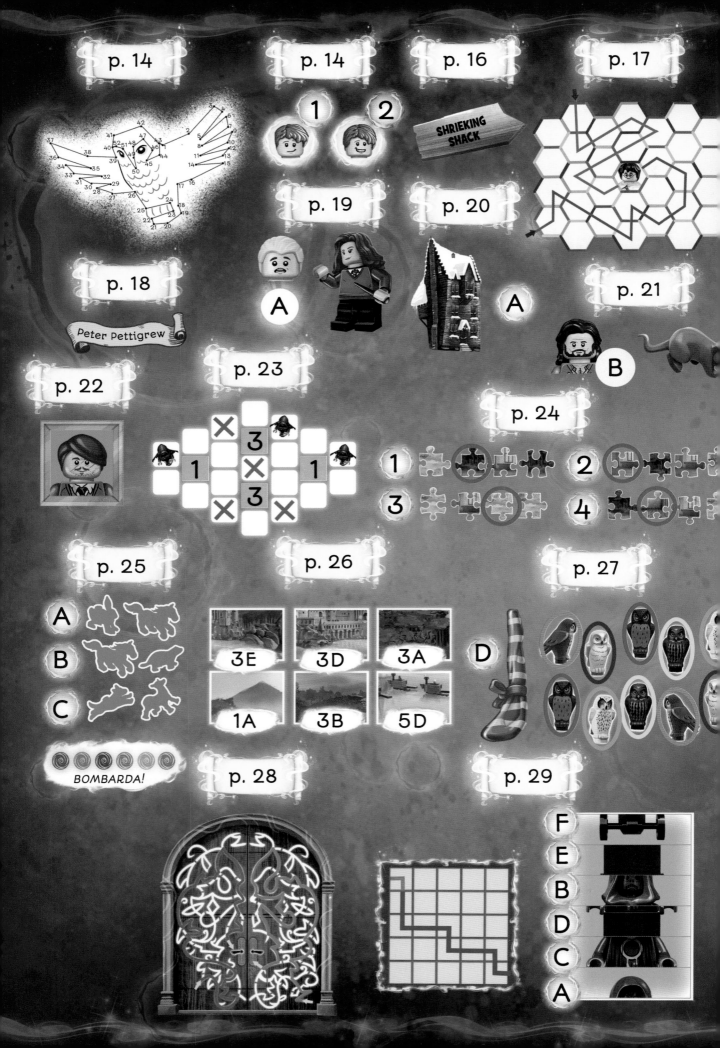